The Norman Rockwell

Family Songbook

The Norman Rockwell Family Songbook

arranged for piano and guitar by

Stephen Dydo and Randa Kirshbaum

with illustrations by Norman Rockwell

Lowe & B. Hould
Publishers

Courtesy Massachusetts
Mutual Life Insurance Company

The publishers wish to thank Marvin Jones of The New York Public
Library (Music Research Division) for his invaluable assistance.

Music engraving by The Music Factory

Published by Borders Press by arrangement with BBS, Inc., and
Harry N. Abrams, Inc., New York.

Borders Press is a division of Borders, Inc.
311 Maynard, Ann Arbor, Michigan, 48104. All rights reserved.

Lowe & B. Hould, Publishers is a trademark of
Borders Properties, Inc.

Library of Congress Catalog Card Number: 96-77442

ISBN: 0-681-22001-5

Printed and bound in Spain
by Artes Gráficas Toledo, S.A.
D.L. TO:895-1996

Contents

Songs of Faith

Holiday Songs

Songs of Social Concern

Patriotic Songs

Fun and Games

American Favorites

The Sidewalks of New York

Moderate waltz

Down in front of Ca-sey's _____ Old brown
That's where John-ny Ca-sey _____ And Lit-tle
Things have changed since those times, _____ Some are

wood-en stoop, _____ On a sum-mer's
Jim-my Crowe, _____ With Jak-ey Kraus, the
up _____ in "G," _____ Oth-ers, they _____ are

eve-ning, _____ We formed a mer-ry group; _____
bak-er _____ Who al-ways had the dough; _____
wan-d'rers _____ But they all feel just like me; _____

town, _____ The tots sang "ring - a - ro - sie," "Lon - don Bridge is
fal - ling down." _____ Boys and girls to - geth - er, _____
Me and Ma - mie O' - Rorke , _____ Tripped the light __ fan - tas - tic
on the side - walks of New York. York.

Yankee Doodle

YANKEE DOODLE CAME TO

Lively

A   E   A   E

1. Oh, Yan - kee Doodle   went to town, u - pon a lit - tle   po - ny. He
2.   Father and I went   down to camp, a - long with Cap-tain   Good - win, And

A   B7   E   A

stuck a fea - ther   in his cap And call'd it ma - ca - ro - ni.
there we saw the   men and boys, As thick as hast-y pud - din'.

RIDING ON A PONY · STUCK A FEATHER IN HIS HAT · AND CALLED IT MACARONI

Yan - kee Doo-dle, keep it up, Yan - kee Doo - dle dan - dy,

Mind the mu - sic and the step and with the girls be han - dy.

Give My Regards to Broadway

Words and music by George M. Cohan

Bright march

1. Did you ev - er see two Yan - kees part up - on a for - eign shore, _____ When the good ship's just a - bout to start for

2. Say hel - lo to dear old Co - ney Isle, if on there you chance to be, _____ When you're at the Wal - dorf, have a smile for and

Chorus:

Give my re - gards to Broad - way, Re -
mem - ber me to Her - ald Square;
Tell all the gang at For - ty Sec - ond Street that
I will soon be there.

Simple Gifts

pli - ci - ty is gained, To bow and to bend we___ shan't be a - shamed. To

turn, turn, will be our de-light, Till by turn - ing, turn - ing we come 'round right.

Midnight Special

see the same damn thing.
and you bet-ter not fight.

Well, it's on-ly one
'Cause the sher-iff will ar -

ta - ble, knife and fork and a pan,
rest you, and he'll car-ry you down,

And if you say a thing a-bout it, you're in trou-ble with the man.
And you can bet your bot-tom dol lar, you're for Su - gar-land bound.

Chorus:

Let the Mid - night Spe - cial shine her light on

23

3. Lord, Thelma said she loved me, but I believe she told a lie,
   'Cause she hasn't been to see me since last July.
   She brought me little coffee, she brought me little tea,
   She brought me nearly everything but the jail house key.

Shenandoah

3. Oh Shenandoah, I'm bound to leave you,
   Chorus: Away, you rolling river.
   Oh Shenandoah, I'll not deceive you,
   Chorus: Away I'm bound to go,
         'Cross the wide Missouri.

4. Oh Shenandoah, I long to hear you,
   Chorus: Away, you rolling river.
   Oh Shenandoah, I long to hear you,
   Chorus: Away I'm bound to go,
         'Cross the wide Missouri.

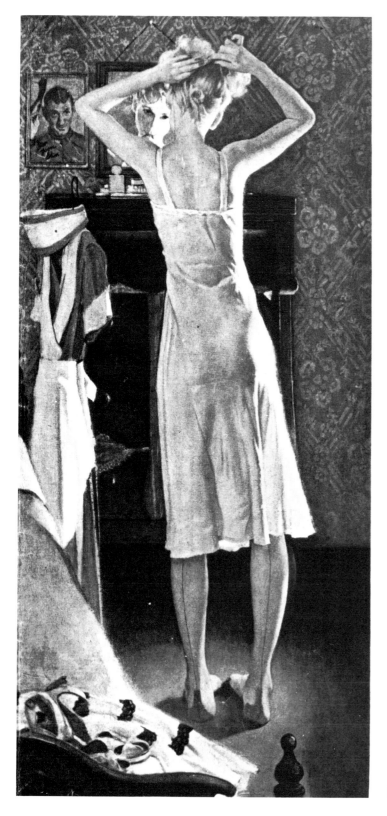

The Band Played On

Words by C. B. Ward
Music by J. F. Palmer

line   Be - hind the man who was their joy and pride. _____

floor   Is   hap - py   mis - sus   Ca - sey now for   life. _____

Chorus:

For _____ Ca - sey would waltz with a straw - ber - ry

blond and the band played on, _____ He'd

glide cross the floor with the girl he a - dor'd and the band

29

played on, _____ But his brain was so load-ed it

near-ly ex-plod-ed, the poor girl would shake with a-larm. _____

He'd ne'er leave the girl with the straw-ber-ry curls, And the

band played on. on. _____

On Top of Old Smokey

Moderately

1. On top of Old Smo - key, _____ All cov - er'd with
2. Now court-in's a pleas - ure, _____ And part - ing is

snow, _____ I lost my true lov -
grief, _____ And a false - heart - ed lov -

er, _____ From a court - in' too slow.
er, _____ Is worse than a thief. _____

Oh, Susanna!

Words and music by Stephen Foster

1. I come from A-la-ba-ma with my ban-jo on my knee, I'm going to Louis-i-a-na, My Su-san-na for to see.
2. It rained all day the night I left, The weath-er it was dry, The sun so hot I froze my-self, Su-san-na don't you cry.

Chorus:

Oh, Su-san-na! Oh, don't you cry for me, For I

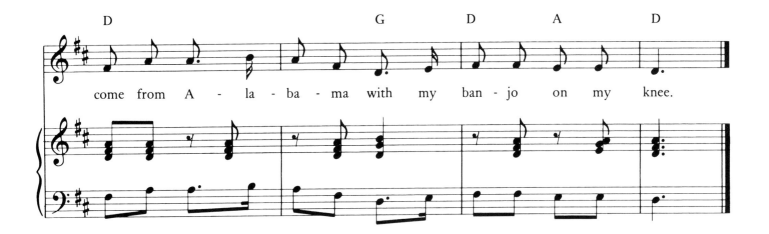

come from A - la - ba - ma with my ban - jo on my knee.

3. I had a dream the other night,
   When everything was still.
   I thought I saw Susanna
   A-comin' down the hill.

4. The red, red rose was in her hand,
   The tear was in her eye,
   I said, "I come from Dixie Land,
   Susanna, don't you cry."

The Blue-Tail Fly

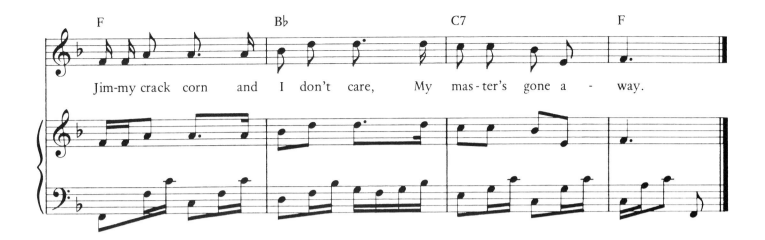

F   B♭   C7   F

Jim-my crack corn and I don't care, My mas-ter's gone a - way.

3. Once when he rode around the farm
The flies about him thick did swarm,
The pony which was very shy
Was bitten by the blue-tail fly.

4. The pony run, he jump, he pitch,
He throw my master in a ditch;
He died and the jury wondered why;
The verdict was, "The blue-tail fly!"

5. They laid him 'neath a 'simmon tree,
His epitaph is there to see:
"Beneath this stone I'm forced to lie,
A victim of the blue-tail fly."

Arkansas Traveler

Words by David Stevens

fid - dler did - n't care, He saw'd a - way at the pop - u - lar air, Tho' his
way it seems to me, You'd bet - ter mend your __ roof," said he. But the

roof tree leak'd like a wa - ter - fall, That did - n't seem to bo - ther the man __ at all.
old man said, as he played a - way: "I could - n't mend it now, it's a rain - y day."

3. The traveler replied: "That's all quite true,
   But this, I think, is the thing for you to do;
   Get busy on a day that is fair and bright,
   Then patch the old roof till it's good and tight."
   But the old man kept on a-playing at his reel,
   And tapp'd the ground with his leathery heel:
   "Get along," said he, "for you give me a pain;
   My cabin never leaks when it doesn't rain."

My Old Kentucky Home

Words and music by Stephen Foster

The sun shines bright on my old Ken-tuck-y home, 'Tis
young folks roll on the lit-tle cab-in floor, All

sum-mer the peo-ple are gay, The corn-top's ripe and the
mer-ry, and hap-py and bright; By'n by hard times come a-

mead-ow's in the bloom, While the birds make mu-sic all the day; The
knock-ing at the door, Then my

Chorus:

old Ken-tuck-y home, good - night!

Weep no more my la - dy, O weep no more to -

day! We will sing one song for the

old Ken-tuck-y home, For the old Ken-tuck-y home, far a - way.

Bill Bailey, Won't You Please Come Home?

Lively

Words and music by Hughie Cannon

"Won't you come home, Bill Bai - ley, won't you come home?"

She cried the whole night long. "I'll do the

dish - es, hon - ey, I'll pay the rent. I know I done you

wrong.   'Mem - ber   that   rain - y   eve - ning

I   drove   you   out   With   noth - in'   but   a   fine - tooth   comb?

___   I   know   I'm   to   blame,   Well   ain't   that   a

shame?   Bill   Bai - ley,   won't   you   please   come   home?"

Swinging on a Star

Words by Johnny Burke
Music by Jimmy Van Heusen

1. A mule is an an-i-mal with long fun-ny ears, He kicks up at an-y-thing he
2. A pig is an an-i-mal with dirt on his face, His shoes are a ter-ri-ble dis-

hears, _____ His back is brawn-y and his brain is weak,_ He's
grace, _____ He's got no man-ners when he eats his food,_ He's

just plain stu-pid with a stub-born streak And by the way, if you hate to go to
fat and la-zy and ex-treme-ly rude, But if you don't care a feath-er or a

school, you may grow up to be a mule. _____ } Or would you
fig, you may grow up to be a pig. _____

The Camptown Races

Words and music by Stephen Foster

1. The Camp-town la - dies sing this song, Doo-dah, doo - dah, The
come down there with my hat caved in, Doo-dah, doo - dah. I

Camp -town race track five miles long, Oh, doo-dah - day! I
go back home with a pock-et full of tin, Oh, doo-dah - day!

Chorus:

Goin' to run all night! Goin' to run all day! I'll____

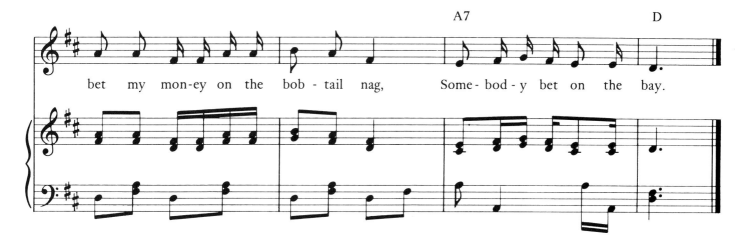

2. The long tail filly and the big black horse, doo-dah, doo-dah,
They flew the track, and both cut across, Oh, doo-dah day.
The blind horse sticking in a big mud hole, doo-dah, doo-dah,
Couldn't touch bottom with a ten-foot pole, Oh, doo-dah day.

Dixie

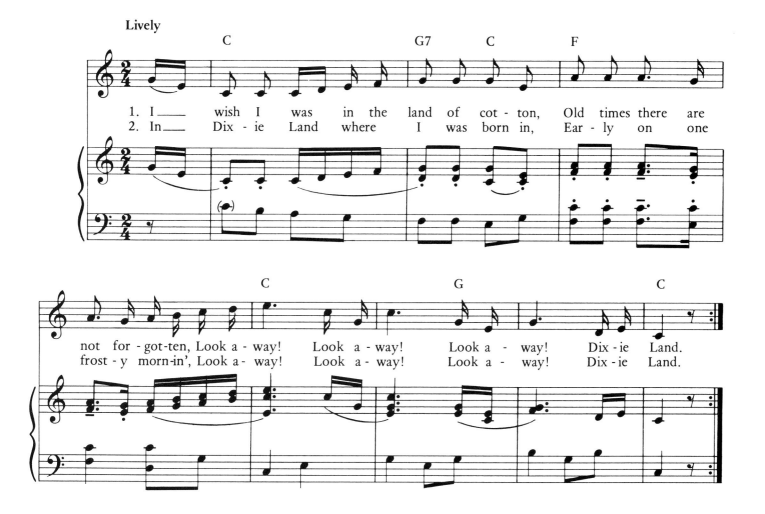

Chorus:

Then I wish I was in Dix - ie, Hoo - ray! Hoo - ray! In Dix - ie Land I'll

take my stand, To live and die in Dix - ie; A - way, a - way, a -

way down south in Dix - ie, A - way, a - way, a - way down south in Dix - ie.

3. There's buckwheat cakes and Injun batter,
   Makes you fat or a little fatter,
   Look away! Look away! Look away! Dixie Land.

4. Then hoe it down and scratch your gravel,
   To Dixie Land I'm bound to travel,
   Look away! Look away! Look away! Dixie Land.

Work Songs

50

Haul Away, Joe

With heavy accents

1. Way, haul a - way,_____ we'll haul a - way the bow - lin'_____
2. Once I had a Span - ish girl, she near - ly drove me cra - zy._____

Chorus:

Way, haul a - way,_____ we'll haul a - way, Joe._____

3. But now I've got a Yankee girl, and she is just a daisy.
4. King Louis was the King of France afore the revolution.
5. But Louis got his head cut off, which spoiled his constitution.
6. Oh, when I was a little boy, and so my mother told me,
7. That if I didn't kiss the girls my lips would all go moldy.
8. Way, haul away, we'll hang and haul together.

Drill, Ye Tarriers, Drill!

Words and music by Thomas Casey

1. Ev- 'ry mor- ning at sev- en o- 'clock There were twen- ty tar- ri- ers a- work- in' at the rock, And the boss comes a- long, and he says, keep still, And come down hea- vy on the cast i- ron drill, And drill, ye tar- ri- ers, drill!

Chorus:

Drill, ye tar-ri-ers, drill! It's work all day for su-gar in your tay, Down be-hind of the rail-way, And drill, ye tar-ri-ers, drill, and blast! and fire!

2. The new foreman was Jim McCann,
   By God, he was a blame mean man!
   Last week an early blast went off,
   And a mile in the air went big Jim Goff,
   And drill, ye tarriers, drill!

3. When next the pay-day came around,
   Jim Goff a dollar short was found.
   "What for?" he asked, came this reply:
   "You're docked for the time you was up in the sky."
   And drill, ye tarriers, drill!

The Farmer Is the Man

Moderately

1. When the farm - er comes to town With his wag - on bro - ken down Oh, the
2. When the law - yer hangs a - round While the butch - er cuts a pound,

farm - er is the man who feeds them all.

If you'll on - ly look and see, I
And the preach - er and the cook Go a

think you will a - gree That the farm - er is the man who feeds them all.
stroll ing by the brook, Oh, the farm - er is the man who feeds them all.

The

farm-er is the man, ___ The farm-er is the man, lives on cred-it till the

fall;

Then they take him by the hand, And they
With the int'-rest rate so high, It's a

lead him from the land, And the mid-dle man's the one who gets it all.
won-der he don't die, For the mort-gage man's the one who gets it all.

The Rock Island Line

G   C

If you ev - er want to ride it, got to ride it like you're

G   D7   G   *Fine*

fly - in'. Buy your tic - ket on the sta - tion on the Rock Is - land Line. ___

1.   A,   B,   C,   dou - ble   X,   Y,   Z,
2. Now Je - sus   died   to   save   our   sins,
3. I   may   be   right and   I   may   be   wrong,   I

D7   G   *D.C.*

Cat's   in   the   cup - board,   but   he   can't   see   me. ___
Glo - ry   be   to   God, we're gon - na   need   Him   a - gain. ___
know you're gon - na   miss   me   when   I   am   gone. ___

Molly Malone

Blow the Man Down

Moderately

1. Oh, __ blow the man down bul - lies, blow the man
2. As __ I was a - walk - ing down Par - a - dise

Chorus:

down! } To me weigh hey blow the man down. { Oh,
Street. }   { A

blow the man down bul - lies, blow him a - way.
pret - ty young dam - sel I chanced for to meet.

Give   me   some   time   to   blow   the   man   down!

3. She was round in the center
   and bluff in the bow,
   Chorus
   So I took in all sail and cried,
   "Way 'nough now."
   Chorus

4. So I tailed her my flipper and
   took her in tow,
   Chorus
   And yardarm to yardarm
   away we did go.
   Chorus

5. But as we were going she said
   unto me,
   Chorus
   "There's a spanking full-rigger
   just ready for sea."
   Chorus

6. But as soon as that packet was
   clear of the bar,
   Chorus
   The mate knocked me down
   with the end of a spar.
   Chorus

7. So I give you fair warning
   before we belay,
   Chorus
   Don't take a heed of what
   pretty girls say.
   Chorus

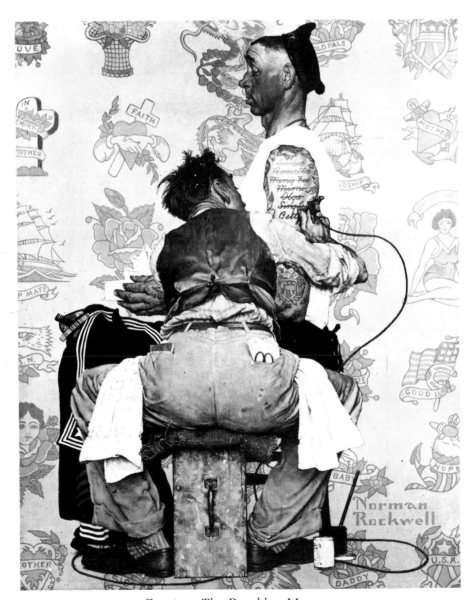

Courtesy The Brooklyn Museum

John Henry

Rhythmically

1. When John Henry was a lit - tle
2. When John Henry was a lit - tle

ba - by   sit - tin' on his pa - pa's   knee,   Well, he
ba - by   sit - tin' on his mo - ma's   knee,   Said the

took   a   ham-mer,___ lit - tle piece of steel, say - in' hammer gonna be the death of ___ me
Big   Bend   Tun-nel on the   C & O   Road   gon-na   be ___ the death of ___ me ___

Em

Lord, Lord, ____ the ham-mer gon-na be the death of - a me. ____
Lord, Lord, ____ gon' be ____ the death of - a me. ____

3. John Henry had a little woman,
   Her name was Mary Magdalene.
   Every day she would sing for John Henry
   Just to hear his hammer when it swing, Lord, Lord,
   Just to hear his hammer when it swing.

4. And now the captain, he says to John Henry,
   "I'm gonna bring that steam drill round,
   I'm gonna bring that steam drill out on the job,
   I'm gonna whop that steel on down, Lord, Lord,
   Gonna whop that steel on down."

5. John Henry said to his captain,
   "I know a man ain't nothin' but a man,
   But before I let your steam drill beat me down,
   I'll die with my hammer in my hand, Lord, Lord,
   I'll die with my hammer in my hand."

6. John Henry said to his shaker,
   "Shaker, why don't you sing?
   And now I'm throwin' forty pounds from my hip on down,
   Listen to that cold steel ring, Lord, Lord,
   Listen to that cold steel ring."

7. John Henry said to his captain,
   "Look-a yonder what I see—
   Steam drill broke, your hole done choke,
   You can't drive steel like me, Lord, Lord,
   You can't drive steel like me."

8. John Henry a-workin' on the mountain,
   Hammer was a-strikin' fire,
   But he work so hard it broke his heart,
   And he laid down his hammer and he died, Lord, Lord,
   He laid down his hammer and he died.

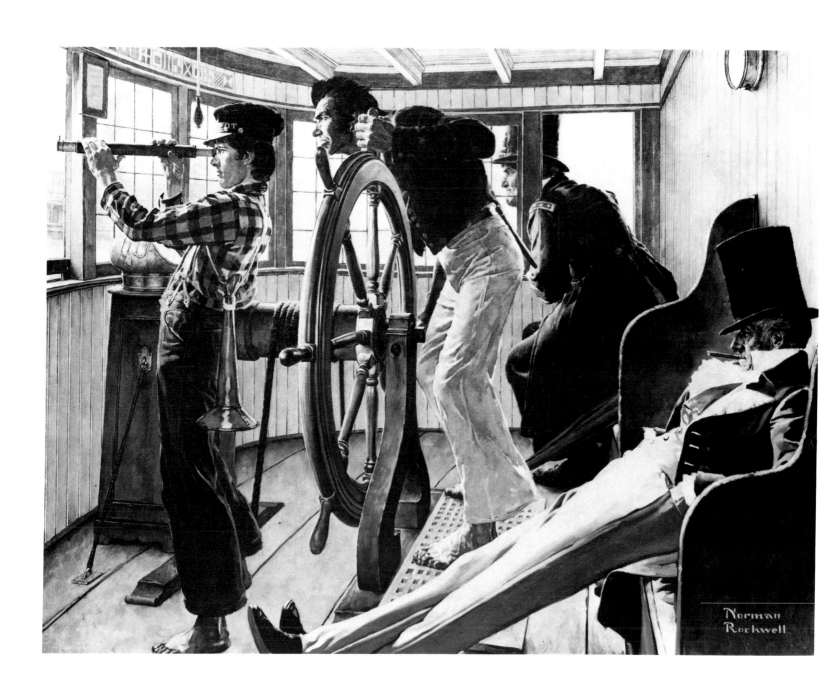

The Erie Canal

* The word "E-ri-e" in this song is pronounced "Ee-rye-ee".

2. We were loaded down with barley,
   We were chuck up full of rye;
   And the captain he looked down at me
   With his goddam wicked eye.

Chorus:

3. Oh the girls are in the Police Gazette,
   The crew are all in jail;
   I'm the only living sea cook's son
   That's left to tell the tale.

Chorus:

Family Songs

Riddle Song

In the Good Old Summer Time

Words and music by Ren Shields and George Evans

good old sum - mer - time, _____ In the good old

sum - mer - time, _____ Strol - ling through the

Personality

Words by Johnny Burke
Music by Jimmy Van Heusen

all the books_ a-bout Du-Bar-ry's looks_ What was it made her the toast_ of Par-ee?__
get some-where in spite of string-y hair_ Or e-ven just a bit bowed at the knee_

She had a well de - vel -oped
If she can show a fault -less

PER -SON-AL -I - TY. _____ And what did Ro -me -o see in
PER -SON-AL -I - TY. _____ And why are cer -tain girls of - fered

Jul -i - et, Or Pi - er -rot in Pi - er -rette, Or Jup -i - ter in
cer -tain things Like sab -le coats and wed -ding rings By men who wear their

Hush, Little Baby

Gently, like a lullaby

1. Hush, lit-tle ba - by, don't say a word, Pa-pa's gon-na buy you a mock-ing bird.
2. If that dia-mond ring turns brass, Pa-pa's gon-na buy you a look-ing glass.

If that mock-ing bird won't sing, Pa-pa's gon-na buy you a dia-mond ring.
If that look-ing glass gets broke, Pa-pa's gon-na buy you a bil-ly goat.

3. If that billy goat won't pull,
   Papa's gonna buy you a cart and bull.
   If that cart and bull turn over,
   Papa's gonna buy you a dog named Rover.

4. If that dog named Rover won't bark,
   Papa's gonna buy you a horse and cart.
   If that horse and cart fall down,
   You'll be the sweetest little baby in town.

Silver Threads Among the Gold

Words by Eben E. Rexford
Music by H. P. Danks

be, will be Al - ways young and fair to me,

lone, a - lone, You have nev - er old - er grown.

Yes! my dar - ling, you will be _____ Al - ways young and fair to me.

Yes! my dar - ling, mine a - lone, _____ You have nev - er old - er grown.

Chorus:

Dar - ling, I am grow - ing, grow - ing old, Sil - ver threads a - mong the gold,

Shine up - on my brow to - day; _____ Life is fad - ing fast a - way.

All Through the Night

1. Sleep, my child and peace at-tend thee, All through the night; Guar-dian an-gels God will send thee, All through the night; Soft the drow-sy hours are creep-ing,

Hill and vale in slumber steeping; I my loving vigil keeping, All through the night.

2. While the moon her watch is keeping
   All through the night;
   While the weary world is sleeping
   All through the night;
   O'er thy spirit gently stealing,
   Visions of delight revealing,
   Breathes a pure and holy feeling
   All through the night.

Hello Central, Give Me Heaven

Words and music by Charles K. Harris

Hel - lo Cen - tral, give me heav - en, For my ma - ma's there,

Courtesy Brown & Bigelow © 1953

When You and I Were Young, Maggie

Words and music by George W. Johnson and James A. Butterfield

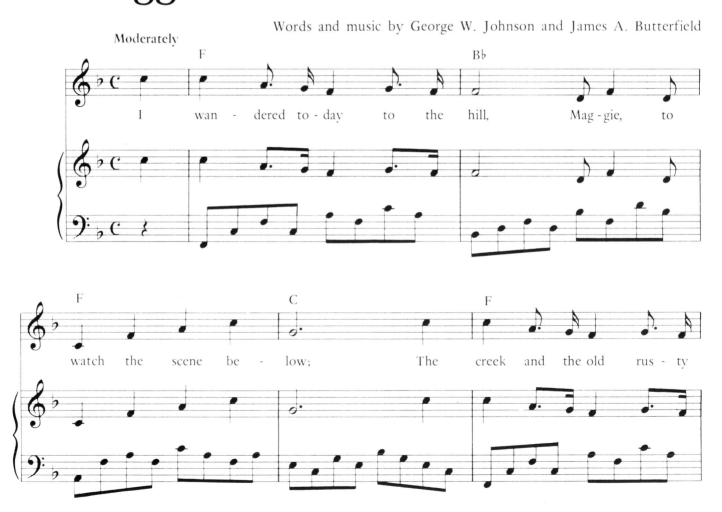

I wan - dered to - day to the hill, Mag - gie, to watch the scene be - low; The creek and the old rus - ty

Old Folks at Home

Words and music by Stephen Foster

1.Way down u-pon the Swan-ee riv-er, Far, far a-way,
All up and down the whole cre-a-tion, Sad-ly I roam,

There's where my heart is turn-ing ev-er; There's where the old folks stay.
Still long-ing for the old plan-ta-tion, And for the old folks at home.

Chorus:

All the world is sad and drear-y Ev'-ry where I roam,

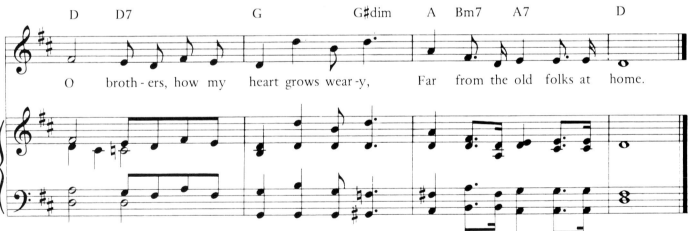

O broth-ers, how my heart grows wear-y, Far from the old folks at home.

2. All around the little farm I wandered when I was young,
   There many happy days I've squandered, there many songs I've sung.
   When I was playing with my brother, happy was I,
   Oh, take me to my kind old mother, there let me live and die.

3. One little hut among the bushes, one that I love,
   Still sadly to my memory rushes, no matter where I rove.
   When will I see the bees a-humming all around the comb,
   When will I hear the banjo tumming, down in my good old home?

Kentucky Babe

Words by Richard Henry Buck
Music by Adam Geibel

Western Songs

Home on the Range

Chorus:

3. Oh, I love those wild flowers in this dear land of ours,
   The curlew, I love to hear scream,
   And I love the white rocks and the antelope flocks
   That graze on the mountain so green.

4. Where the air is so pure and the zephyrs so free,
   The breezes so balmy and light
   That I would not exchange my home on the range
   For all of the cities so bright.

The Streets of Laredo

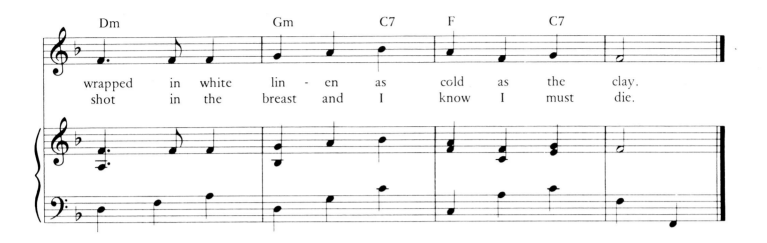

wrapped   in   white   lin - en   as   cold   as   the   clay.
shot   in   the   breast   and   I   know   I   must   die.

3. " 'Twas once in the saddle I used to go dashing,
    'Twas once in the saddle I used to go gay;
    'Twas first to go drinking, and then to card playing,
    Got shot in the breast and I'm dying today."

4. "Get six jolly cowboys to carry my coffin,
    Get six pretty maidens to carry my pall;
    Put bunches of roses all over my coffin,
    Roses to deaden the clods as they fall."

5. "Oh, beat the drum slowly, and play the fife lowly,
    And play the dead march as you bear me along;
    Take me to the valley and lay the sod o'er me,
    For I'm a young cowboy and I know I've done wrong."

6. We beat the drum slowly and played the fife lowly,
    And bitterly wept as we bore him along,
    For we loved our comrade, so brave, young, and handsome,
    We all loved our comrade although he'd done wrong.

The Yellow Rose of Texas

Lively

G

1. There's a yel-low rose in Tex - as I'm go - ing there to see. No
2. Where the Ri - o Grande is flow-ing, Where stars are shin - ing bright, We
3. Oh I'm go - ing back to find her. My heart is full of woe; We'll

D7

oth - er sol - dier knows her, No - bo - dy on - ly me. She
walked a - long the riv - er, On a qui - et sum - mer night. She
sing the songs to - geth - er We sang so long a - go. I'll

G

cried so when I left her, It al - most broke my heart, And
said, "If you re - mem - ber, We part - ed long a - go; you
play the ban - jo gai - ly, And sing the song of yore. This

Buffalo Gals

C   G7

1. As I was walk-ing down the street, down the street,

C

down the street, A pret-ty lit-tle girl I chanced to meet, and we

G7   C   *Chorus:*

danced by the light of the moon. Buf-fa-lo gals won't you come out to-night,

102

come out to-night come out to-night? Buf-fa-lo gals won't you come out to-night, and dance by the light of the moon?

G7   Dm7   C   G7   C

2. I asked her if she'd stop and talk, stop and talk, stop and talk,
Her feet took up the whole sidewalk, and left no room for me.

3. I asked her if she'd be my wife, be my wife, be my wife,
Then I'd be happy all my life, if she'd marry me.

Bury Me Not on the Lone Prairie

Slowly
F

1. "Oh, bu-ry me not   on the lone prai-rie,"
2. "Oh, bu-ry me not   on the lone prai-rie,"

3. "I've always wished to be laid when I died
   In the little churchyard on the green hillside;
   By my father's grave there let mine be,
   And bury me not on the lone prairie."

4. "Oh, bury me not"— and his voice failed there,
   But we took no heed of his dying prayer.
   In a narrow grave, just six by three,
   We buried him on the lone prairie.

5. And the cowboys now, as they roam the plain,
   (For they marked the spot where his bones were lain),
   Fling a handful of roses over the grave,
   With a prayer to Him who his soul will save.

6. "Oh, bury me not on the lone prairie,
   Where the wolves can howl and growl o'er me.
   Fling a handful of roses over my grave,
   With a prayer to Him who my soul will save."

I Ride an Old Paint

Sweet Betsy from Pike

old yal - ler dog? }
Pike coun - ty rose. }
Sing__ too - ra - li - oo - ra - li - oo - ra - li -

ay, Sing__ too - ra - li - oo - ra - li - oo - ra - li - ay.

3. They swam the wide rivers and crossed the tall peaks,
And camped on the prairie for weeks upon weeks,
Starvation and cholera and hard work and slaughter,
They reached California spite of hell and high water.

4. Out on the prairie one bright starry night
They broke out the whiskey and Betsy got tight,
She sang and she shouted and danced o'er the plain,
And showed her bare arse to the whole wagon train.

5. The Injuns came down in a wild yelling horde,
And Betsy was skeered they would scalp her adored;
Behind the front wheel Betsy did crawl,
And there she fought the Injuns with musket and ball.

6. The alkali desert was burning and bare,
And Isaac's soul shrank from the death that lurked there:
"Dear Old Pike County, I'll go back to you."
Said Betsy, "You'll go by yourself if you do."

Red River Valley

Slowly rolling

1. From this val - ley they say you are go - ing, _____ We will
2. Won't you think of the val - ley you're leav - ing? _____ Oh, how

miss your bright eyes and sweet smile, For they say you are tak - ing the
lone - ly, how sad it will be, Oh __ think of the fond heart you're

sun-shine, _____ That bright - ens our path - way a - while. ____
break -ing, _____ And the grief you are caus - ing me. ____

Come and sit by my side if you love me, _____ Do not
has - ten to bid me a - dieu, But re - mem - ber the Red Riv - er
Val - ley, _____ And the girl that has loved you so true. _____

Git Along, Little Dogies

Chorus:

Verse (fine)

113

spring comes a - long   we round up the do - gies,

Clip off their fur   and bob off their__ tails,

Pick out the strays   then the herd is in - spect - ed, and the

repeat to Chorus

ver - y next day we go out on the trail. Yip - pee

114

Love Songs

norman Rockwell

Scarborough Fair

Sweet Genevieve

Words by George Cooper
Music by Henry Tucker

1. Oh Gen - e - vieve I'd give the world To live a - gain the love - ly past. The
rose of youth was dew - im - pearled; But now it with - ers in the blast. I
see thy face in ev - 'ry dream, My wak - ing thoughts are full of thee; Thy

2. Fair Genevieve, my early love,
   The years but make thee dearer far!
   My heart shall never, never rove,
   Thou art my only guiding star.
   For me the past has no regret,
   Whate'er the years may bring to me;
   I bless the hour when we first met,
   The hour that gave me love and thee.

Oh, Promise Me

Words by Clement Scott
Music by R. de Koven

Oh, prom-ise me that some day you and I Will

take our love to-geth-er to some sky Where we can be a-lone, and faith re-

might - y mu - sic to our ver - y souls; No love less per - fect than a

life with thee; Oh prom - ise me! oh prom - ise me!

Sunday, Monday, or Always

Words by Johnny Burke
Music by Jimmy Van Heusen

Aura Lee

Words by W. W. Fosdick
Music by George R. Poulton

Slowly

1. As the black-bird in the spring, 'Neath the wil-low tree, _____

Sat and piped, I heard him sing, Sing-ing Au - ra Lee.

Au - ra Lee, Au - ra Lee, Maid with gol-den hair,

Sun-shine came a - long with thee, And swal-lows in the air.

2. Take my heart and take my ring,
   I give my all to thee,
   Take me for eternity,
   Dearest Aura Lee!
   Aura Lee, Aura Lee,
   Maid with golden hair,
   Sunshine came along with thee,
   And swallows in the air.

3. In her blush the rose was born,
   'Twas music when she spake,
   In her eyes, the light of morn,
   Sparkling, seemed to break.
   Aura Lee, Aura Lee,
   Maid with golden hair,
   Sunshine came along with thee,
   And swallows in the air.

4. Aura Lee, the bird may flee
   The willow's golden hair,
   Then the wintry winds may be
   Blowing ev'rywhere.
   Yet if thy blue eyes I see,
   Gloom will soon depart,
   For to me, sweet Aura Lee
   Is sunshine to the heart.

Daisy Bell

Words and music by Harry Dacre

Wheth - er she loves me or loves me not,
When the road's dark we can both des - pise

Some - times it's
P'lice - men and

hard to tell; _____
"lamps" as well; _____

Yet I am long - ing to
There are "bright lights" in the

share the lot Of beau - ti - ful Dai - sy Bell! _____
daz - zling eyes Of beau - ti - ful Dai - sy Bell! _____

Chorus:

Dai - sy, Dai - sy, Give me your

On the seat of a bi-cy-cle built for two. _____

3. I will stand by you in "wheel" or woe,
Daisy, Daisy!
You'll be the belle which I'll ring, you know!
Sweet little Daisy Bell!
You'll take the "lead" in each "trip" we take,
Then, if I don't do well,
I will permit you to use the brake,
My beautiful Daisy Bell!

Black Is the Color

Slowly

1. But black is the col-or _____ of my true love's hair. _____ Her lips are like _____ a

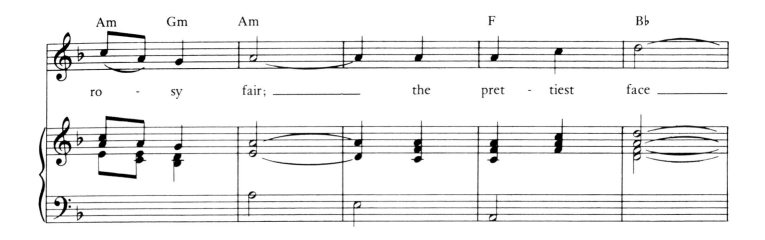

ro - sy fair; _____ the pret - tiest face _____

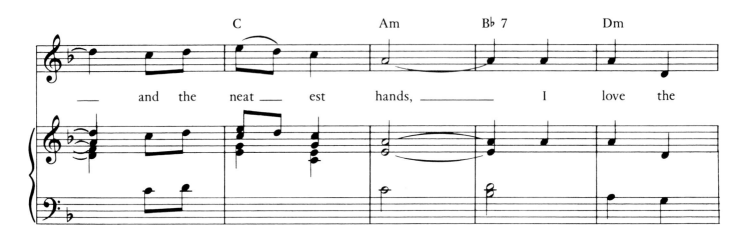

_____ and the neat ___ est hands, _____ I love the

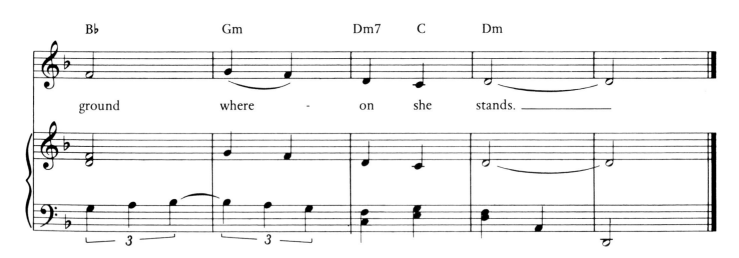

ground where - on she stands. _____

2. I got to the Clyde for to mourn and weep,
   But satisfied I never sleep;
   I'll write to you in a few short lines,
   I'll suffer death ten thousand times.

3. I love my love and well she knows.
   I love the ground whereon she goes.
   If you no more on earth I see,
   I can't serve you as you have me.

My Bonnie Lies over the Ocean

Greensleeves

Green - sleeves was my heart of gold,___ And who but my la - dy Green - sleeves.

2. I long have waited at your hand
   To do your bidding as your slave,
   And waged, have I, both life and land
   Your love and affection to have.

3. If you intend thus to disdain
   It does the more enrapture me,
   And even so, I will remain
   Your lover in captivity.

4. Alas, my love, that yours should be
   A heart of faithless vanity,
   So here I meditate all alone
   Upon your insincerity.

5. Ah, Greensleeves, now farewell, adieu,
   To God I pray to prosper thee,
   For I remain thy lover true,
   Come once again and be with me.

Down in the Valley

Slowly

1. Down in the val - ley, the val - ley so low, _____ Hang your head o - ver, hear the wind blow, _____ Hear the wind blow, dear, hear the wind blow, _____ Hang your head o - ver, hear the wind blow. _____
2. Ros - es love sun - shine, vi - o - lets love dew, _____ An - gels in hea - ven know I love you, _____ Know I love you, dear, know I love you, _____ An - gels in hea - ven know I love you. _____
3. Write me a let - ter, con - tain - ing three lines, _____ An - swer my ques - tion, will you be mine? _____ Will you be mine, dear, will you be mine? _____ An - swer my ques - tion, will you be mine? _____

Beautiful Dreamer

Words and music by Stephen Foster

1. Beau - ti - ful dream - er, wake un - to me,
2. Beau - ti - ful dream - er, out on the sea,

Star-light and dew - drops are wait - ing for thee. _____ Sounds of the rude world
Mer-maids are chant - ing the wild Lor - e - lei, _____ O - ver the stream - let

heard in the day, Lulled by the moon - light have all passed a
va - pors are borne, Wait - ing to fade at the bright com - ing

Jeanie with the Light Brown Hair

Words and music by Stephen Foster

1. I dream of Jean-ie with the light brown hair,
2. I long for Jean-ie with the day-dawn smile,

Borne, like a va - por, on the sum-mer's air. I see her trip-ping where the
Rad - iant in glad - ness, warm with win-ning guile? I hear her mel - o - dies, like

bright streams play, Hap-py as the dai - sies that dance on her way.
joys gone by, Sigh-ing round my heart o'er the fond hopes that die;

But Beautiful

Words by Johnny Burke
Music by Jimmy Van Heusen

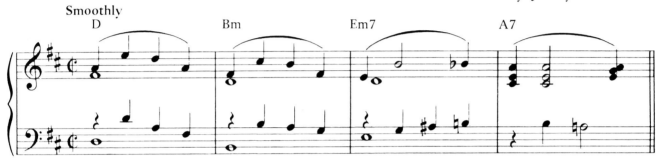

Who can say what love is? Does it start

in the mind or the heart?

I Love You Truly

Words and music by Carrie Jacobs Bond

Andante con amore

I love you tru - ly, tru - ly, dear, Life with its sor - row, Life with its tear, Fades in - to dreams when I feel you are near, For I love you tru - ly, tru - ly

Songs of Faith

Amazing Grace

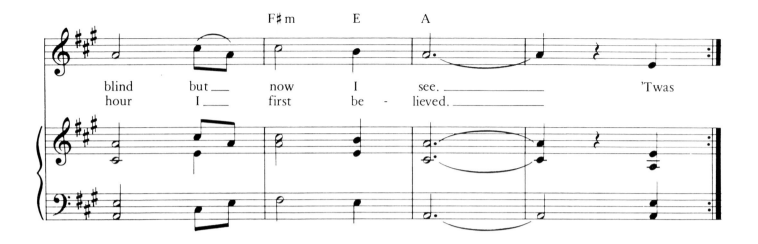

blind but __ now I see. _____ 'Twas
hour I __ first be - lieved. _____

2. Through many dangers, toils and snares,
   I have already come.
   'Tis grace that brought me safe thus far,
   And grace will lead me home.

3. How sweet the name of Jesus sounds,
   In a believer's ear.
   It soothes his sorrows, heals his wounds,
   And drives away his fear.

4. When we've been there ten thousand years,
   Bright shining as the sun,
   We've no less days to sing God's praise,
   Than when we first begun.

Go Tell It on the Mountains

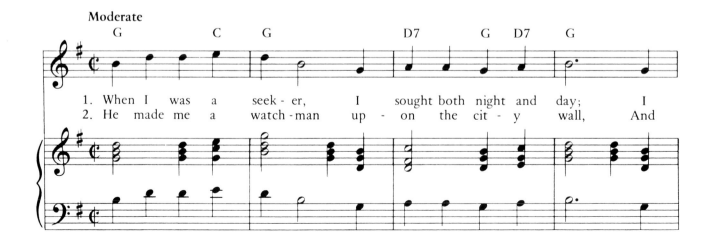

1. When I was a seek - er, I sought both night and day; I
2. He made me a watch - man up - on the cit - y wall, And

asked the Lord to help me, And He showed me the way. _____
if I serve him tru - ly, I am the least of all. _____

Chorus:

Go tell it on the moun - tains, O - ver the hills and ev - 'ry where;_

Go tell it on the moun - tains that Je - sus Christ_ is born.

3. He made me a watchman
Upon the city wall,
And if I am a Christian,
I am the least of all.

4. And, lo, when they had seen it,
They all bowed down and prayed;
Then traveled on together
To where the babe was laid.

Kum Ba Yah

All God's Children Got Shoes

4. I got a song, you got a song,
   All God's children got songs.
   When I get to heaven gonna sing my song,
   Gonna sing all over God's heaven, *etc.*

5. I got wings, you got wings,
   All God's children got wings.
   When I get to heaven gonna put on my wings,
   Gonna fly all over God's heaven, *etc.*

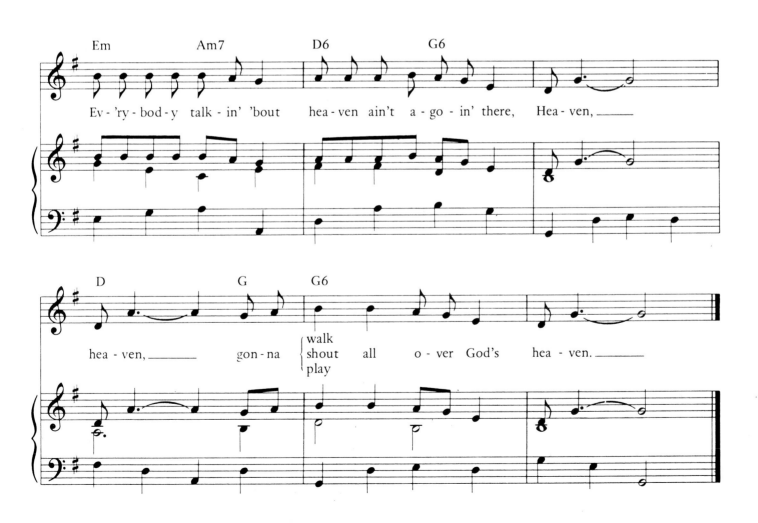

Ev - 'ry - bod - y talk - in' 'bout hea - ven ain't a - go - in' there, Hea - ven,____

hea - ven,____ gon - na {walk/shout/play} all o - ver God's hea - ven.____

When the Saints Go Marching In

Swing Low, Sweet Chariot

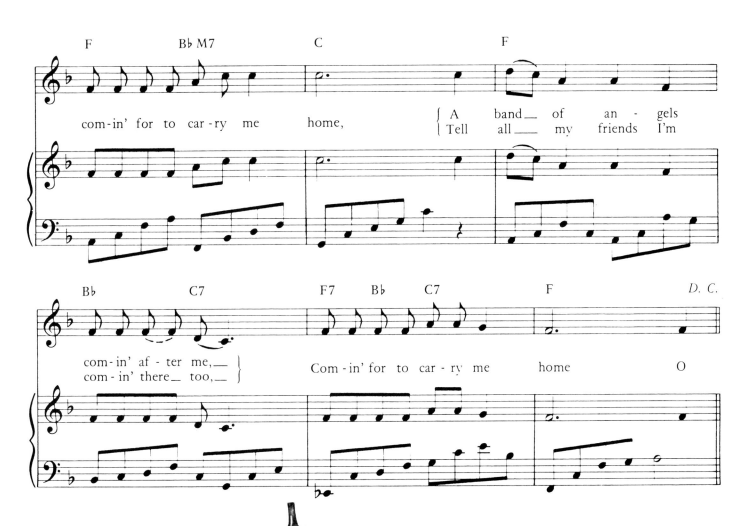

com-in' for to car-ry me home,
{ A band of an - gels
{ Tell all my friends I'm

com-in' af - ter me,
com-in' there too,
Com-in' for to car-ry me home O

3. The brightest day that ever I saw,
Comin' for to carry me home.
When Jesus washed my sins away,
Comin' for to carry me home.

4. I'm sometimes up and sometimes down,
Comin' for to carry me home.
But still my soul feels heaven bound,
Comin' for to carry me home.

5. I never went to heaven, but I've been told,
Comin' for to carry me home.
The streets in heaven are paved with gold,
Comin' for to carry me home.

Sometimes I Feel like a Motherless Child

Nobody Knows the Trouble I've Seen

Moderately

No-bod-y knows the trou-ble I've seen, No-bod-y knows but

Je - sus. No-bod-y knows the trou-ble I've seen, Glo-ry hal-le -

3. One day when I was walkin' along,
   Oh, yes, Lord;
   The sky opened up and love came down,
   Oh, yes, Lord.

4. What makes old Satan hate me so,
   Oh, yes, Lord;
   He had me once and had to let me go,
   Oh, yes, Lord.

5. I never shall forget that day,
   Oh, yes, Lord;
   When Jesus washed my sins away,
   Oh, yes, Lord.

We Gather Together

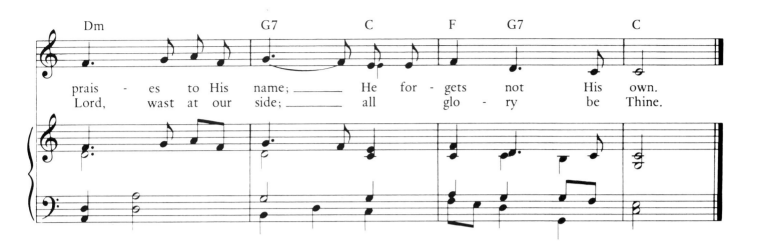

prais - es to His name; _____ He for - gets not His own.
Lord, wast at our side; _____ all glo - ry be Thine.

3. We all do extol thee, Thou leader triumphant,
   And pray that Thou still our Defender will be.
   Let Thy congregation escape tribulation;
   Thy Name be ever praised! Oh Lord, make us free!

Courtesy Massachusetts Mutual Life Insurance Company

Now the Day Is Over

Words by Sabine Baring-Gould
Music by Joseph Barnby

1. Now the day is o - ver, Night is draw - ing nigh;
2. Je - sus, give the wea - ry Calm and sweet re - pose,
3. When the morn - ing wa - kens, Then may we a - rise

Sha - dows of the eve - ning Steal a - cross the sky.
With thy tend - 'rest bless - ing, May our eye - lids close.
Pure and fresh and sin - less In Thy ho - ly eyes.

Holidays

Joy to the World

Words by Isaac Watts

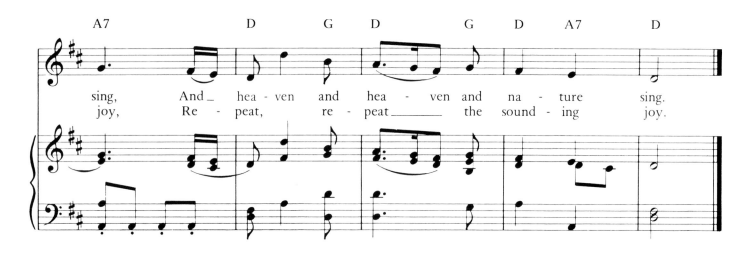

sing,   And _ hea - ven and hea - ven and na - ture   sing.
joy,   Re - peat,   re - peat_____ the sound - ing   joy.

3. He rules the world with truth and grace,
   And makes the nations prove
   The glories of His righteousness,
   The wonders of His love.

Silent Night

Music by Franz Gruber

1. Si - lent night,   ho - ly night! All is calm,
2. Si - lent night,   ho - ly night! Shep - herds quake
3. Si - lent night,   ho - ly night! Child of heav'n,

Oh Come, All Ye Faithful

Chorus:

Oh come, let us a - dore Him, Oh come, let us a - dore Him, Oh come let us a - dore Him, ___ Christ ___ the Lord.

3. Yea, Lord, we greet thee, born this happy morning,
   Jesus, to Thee be glory giv'n;
   Word of the Father, now in flesh appearing:
       Oh, come, *etc.*

4. *Adeste fideles, laeti triumphantes;*
   Venite, venite in Bethlehem:
   Natum videte, Regem angelorum:
   Venite adoremus, venite adoremus,
   Venite adoremus Dominum.

Over the River

through the woods, Oh how the wind does blow! _____ It
through the woods, Trot fast my dap - ple gray! _____ Spring
through the woods, Now grand - mo - ther's cap I spy! _____ Hur -

stings the toes And bites the nose, As o - ver the ground we go. _____
o - ver the ground, Like a hunt - ing hound! For this is Thanks - giv - ing Day. _____
rah for the fun! Is the pud - ding done? Hur - rah for the pump - kin pie! _____

Up on the Housetop

Words and music by Benjamin R. Hanby

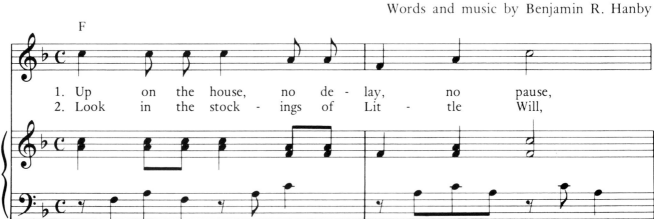

1. Up on the house, no de - lay, no pause,
2. Look in the stock - ings of Lit - tle Will,

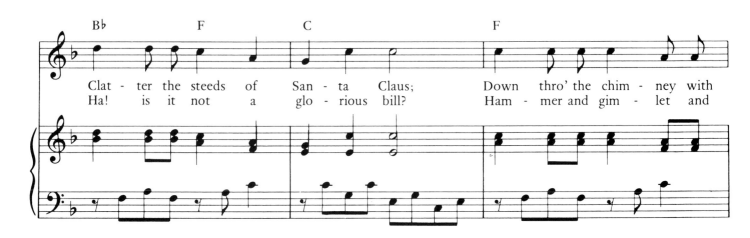

Clat - ter the steeds of San - ta Claus; Down thro' the chim - ney with
Ha! is it not a glo - rious bill? Ham - mer and gim - let and

loads of toys,
Ho for the lit - tle ones, Christ - mas joys.

lots of tacks,
Whis - tle and whir-li - gig, whip that cracks.

Chorus:

Ho, ho, ho! Who would-n't go, Ho, ho, ho! Who would-n't go, ——

Up on the house top, click, click, click! Down thro' the chim - ney with good St. Nick.

3. Snow-white stocking of Little Nell,
   Oh, pretty Santa, cram it well!
   Leave her a dolly that laughs and cries,
   One that can open and shut its eyes.

4. Pa, Ma, and Uncle and Grandma too,
   All, I declare, have something new;
   Even the baby enjoys his part,
   Shaking a rattle, now bless his heart.

The Twelve Days of Christmas

1. On the first day of Christ-mas my true love gave to me, A par-tridge in a pear tree.

2. On the sec - ond
3. On the third } day of Christ - mas my true love sent to me,
4. On the fourth

2.3.4. Two tur - tle doves, } and a par-tridge___ in a pear tree.
3.4. Three French___ hens,
4. Four call - ing birds,

(Sing in reverse order for verses indicated)

187

Halloween Song

night.   To - night   is   Hal - low - e'en. _____

It Came upon a Midnight Clear

Words by Edmund H. Sears
Music by Richard S. Willis

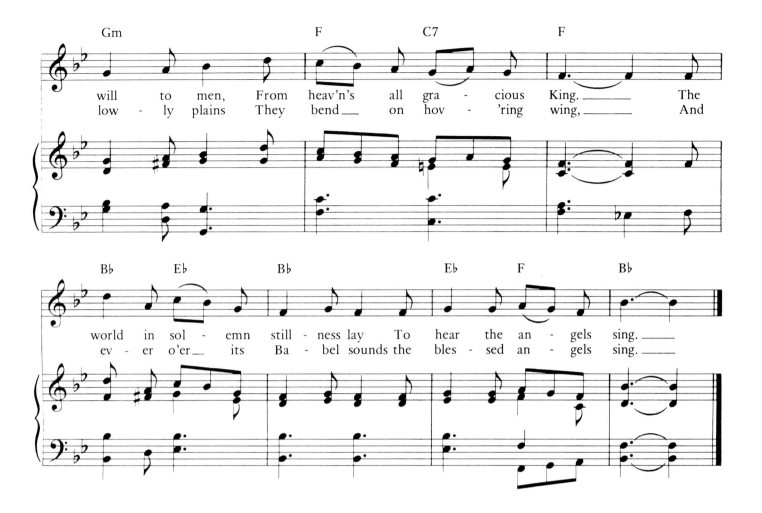

will to men, From heav'n's all gra - cious King. _____ The
low - ly plains They bend __ on hov - 'ring wing, _____ And

world in sol - emn still - ness lay To hear the an - gels sing. _____
ev - er o'er __ its Ba - bel sounds the bles - sed an - gels sing. _____

3. O ye, beneath life's crushing load
   Whose forms are bending low,
   Who toil along the climbing way
   With painful steps and slow
   Look now! for glad and golden hours
   Come swiftly on the wing;
   O rest beside the weary road
   And hear the angels sing.

4. For lo! the days are hastening on,
   By prophet bards foretold,
   When with the ever-circling years
   Comes round the age of gold;
   When peace shall over all the earth
   Its ancient splendors fling;
   And the whole world give back the song
   Which now the angels sing.

On the First Thanksgiving Day

On the first Thanks - giv - ing day Pil - grims went to church to pray,

Thanked the Lord for sun and rain, Thanked Him for the fields of grain.

Now Thanksgiv - ing comes a - gain; Praise the Lord as they did then,

Thank Him for the sun and rain, Thank Him for the fields of grain.

The First Noel

2. They looked up and saw a Star
   Shining in the East, beyond them far,
   And to the earth it gave great light,
   And so it continued both day and night.

3. This star drew nigh to the northwest,
   O'er Bethlehem it took its rest.
   And there it did both stop and stay,
   Right over the place where Jesus lay.

4. Then enter'd in there wise men three,
   Full rev'rently upon their knee,
   And offer'd there in His presence,
   Their gold and myrrh and frankincense.

Jingle Bells

Words and music by James Pierpont

Songs of Social Concern

DO UNTO OTHERS
AS YOU WOULD HAVE THEM
DO UNTO YOU

We're Tenting Tonight

Words and music by Walter Kittredge

1. We're tent - ing to - night on the old camp - ground,
2. We've been tent - ing to - night on the old camp - ground,

Give us a song to cheer Our wear - y hearts, a
Think - ing of days gone by, Of the loved ones at home that

song of home, And friends we love so dear.
gave us the hand, And the tears that said "Good - bye!"

Go Down, Moses

Slowly

1. When Israel was in Egypt's land, } Let my people
2. Thus spoke the Lord, bold Moses said,

go, Oppressed so hard they could not stand, } Let my people go.
If not I'll smite your first-born dead,

Chorus:

Go down, Moses, Way down in Egypt's land,

Tell old _____ Pha - roah ___ To let my peo - ple go.

3. The Lord told Moses what to do,
   Let my people go,
   To lead the Hebrew children through,
   Let my people go.

4. O come along Moses, you won't get lost,
   Let my people go,
   Stretch out your rod and come across,
   Let my people go.

5. Your foes shall not before you stand,
   Let my people go,
   And you'll possess fair Canaan's Land,
   Let my people go.

6. We need not always weep and mourn,
   Let my people go,
   And wear these slavery chains forlorn,
   Let my people go.

Down by the Riverside

lay down my sword and shield
walk with the Prince of Peace
Down by the ri - ver - side, ___
down by the ri - ver - side. _____ I ain't gon - na
stu - dy war no more, I ain't gon - na stu - dy war no more, I ain't gon - na

3. Gonna put on my starry crown,
   Down by the riverside, down by the riverside,
   Down by the riverside.
   Gonna put on my starry crown,
   Down by the riverside,
   And study war no more.

4. Gonna put on my golden shoes,
   Down by the riverside, down by the riverside,
   Down by the riverside.
   Gonna put on my golden shoes,
   Down by the riverside,
   And study war no more.

Patriotic Songs

SESQUI·CENTENNIAL·CELEBRA[...]N
OF·THE·SIGNING·OF·TH[...]
DECLARATION·OF·INDEPENDE[...]CE

Norman
Rockwell

America

Words by Samuel Francis Smith

Battle Hymn of the Republic

Words by Julia Ward Howe

1. Mine eyes have seen the glo - ry of the
2. I have seen Him in the watch - fires of a

com - ing of the Lord; he is tramp - ling out the vin - tage where the
hun - dred circ - ling camps; They have build - ed Him an al - tar in the

grapes of wrath are stored; He hath loos'd the fate - ful light - ning of His
ev - 'ning dews and damps; I can read His right - eous sen - tence by the

ter - ri - ble swift sword, His truth is march - ing on.
dim and flar - ing lamps, His day is march - ing on.

Chorus:

Glo - ry, glo - ry Hal - le - lu - jah! Glo - ry, glo - ry Hal - le - lu - jah!

Glo - ry, glo - ry Hal - le - lu - jah! His truth is march - ing on.

John Brown's Body

(Sung to the tune of "Battle Hymn of the Republic")

1. John Brown's body lies a-mouldrin' in the grave,
   John Brown's body lies a-mouldrin' in the grave,
   John Brown's body lies a-mouldrin' in the grave,
   But his soul goes marching on.

2. The stars above in heaven are a-lookin' kindly down,
   The stars above in heaven are a-lookin' kindly down,
   The stars above in heaven are a-lookin' kindly down,
   On the grave of old John Brown.

3. He captured Harper's Ferry with his nineteen men so true,
   He frightened Old Virginia till she trembled through and through,
   They hanged him for a traitor, they themselves the traitor crew,
   But his soul goes marching on.

4. Well, he's gone to be a soldier in the army of the Lord,
   Well, he's gone to be a soldier in the army of the Lord,
   Well, he's gone to be a soldier in the army of the Lord,
   But his soul goes marching on.

Chorus
   Glory, glory hallelujah,
   Glory, glory hallelujah,
   Glory, glory hallelujah,
   His soul goes marching on!

The Caissons Go Rolling Along

Words and music by Brig. Gen. Edmund L. Gruber

1. O - ver hill, o - ver dale, We have hit the dus - ty trail, And those
2. To the front, day and night, Where the dough - boys dig and fight, And those

cais - sons go rol - ling a - long. _____ In and out, hear them shout: "Coun - ter
cais - sons go rol - ling a - long. _____ Our bar - rage will be there, fired

march and right a - bout," As the cais - sons go rol - ling a - long. _____
On the roc - ket's flare As the cais - sons go rol - ling a - long. _____

The Star-Spangled Banner

Words by Francis Scott Key

America the Beautiful

Words by Katherine Lee Bates
Music by Samuel A. Ward

With dignity

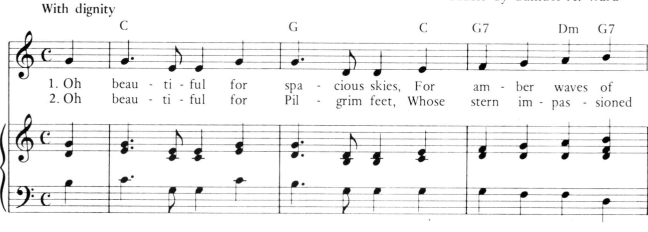

1. Oh beau - ti - ful for spa - cious skies, For am - ber waves of
2. Oh beau - ti - ful for Pil - grim feet, Whose stern im - pas - sioned

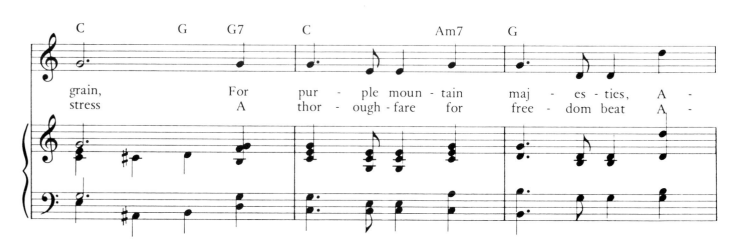

grain, For pur - ple moun - tain maj - es - ties, A -
stress A thor - ough - fare for free - dom beat A -

3. Oh beautiful for heroes proved
   In liberating strife,
   Who more than self their country loved,
   And mercy more than life.
   America! America!
   May God thy gold refine,
   Till all success be nobleness,
   And every gain divine.

4. Oh beautiful for patriot dream
   That sees beyond the years,
   Thine alabaster cities gleam,
   Undimmed by human tears.
   America! America!
   God shed his grace on thee,
   And crown thy good with brotherhood
   From sea to shining sea.

The Landing of the Pilgrims

Words by Felicia Hemans

Moderately

1. The break-ing waves dashed high On a stern and rock-bound coast, And the
2. Not as the con-quer-or comes, They, the true-heart-ed, came; Not

woods a-gainst a storm-y sky Their gi-ant branch-es tossed; And the
with the roll of stir-ring drums, And the trum-pet that sings of fame; Not

hea-vy night hung dark ____ The ____ hills and wa-ters o'er, ____ When a
as the flee-ing come, ____ In ____ si-lence and in fear; ____ They

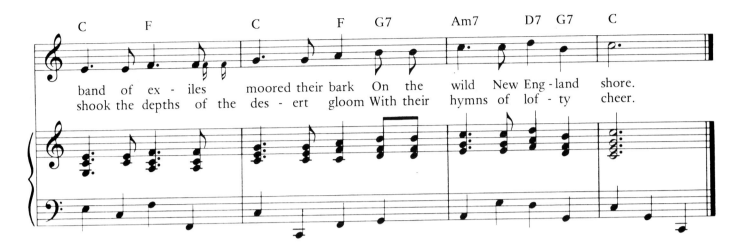

band of ex - iles moored their bark On the wild New Eng - land shore.
shook the depths of the des - ert gloom With their hymns of lof - ty cheer.

Marines' Hymn

1. From the halls of Mon-te-zu---ma to the shores of Tri-po-li, ___ We___ fight our coun-try's bat---tles on the land and
2. Our flag's un-furled to ev---'ry breeze from ___ dawn to set-ting sun; ___ We have fought in ev---'ry clime and place where___ we could
3. Here's a health to you and to our corps, which ___ we are proud to serve; ___ In___ ma-ny a strife we've fought for life, and___ ne---ver

on the sea. _____ First to fight for right and
take a gun. _____ In the snow of far-off
lost our nerve. _____ If the Ar - my and the

free - - dom and to keep our hon - or
nor - - thern lands and in sun - ny tro - pic
Na - - vy ev - er looked on hea - ven's

clean, _____ We are proud to claim the ti - -
scenes, _____ You will find us al - ways on the
scenes, _____ They would find the streets are guard - -

tle of U - ni - ted States Ma - rines. _____
job, the U - ni - ted States Ma - rines. _____
ed by U - ni - ted States Ma - rines. _____

Fun and Games

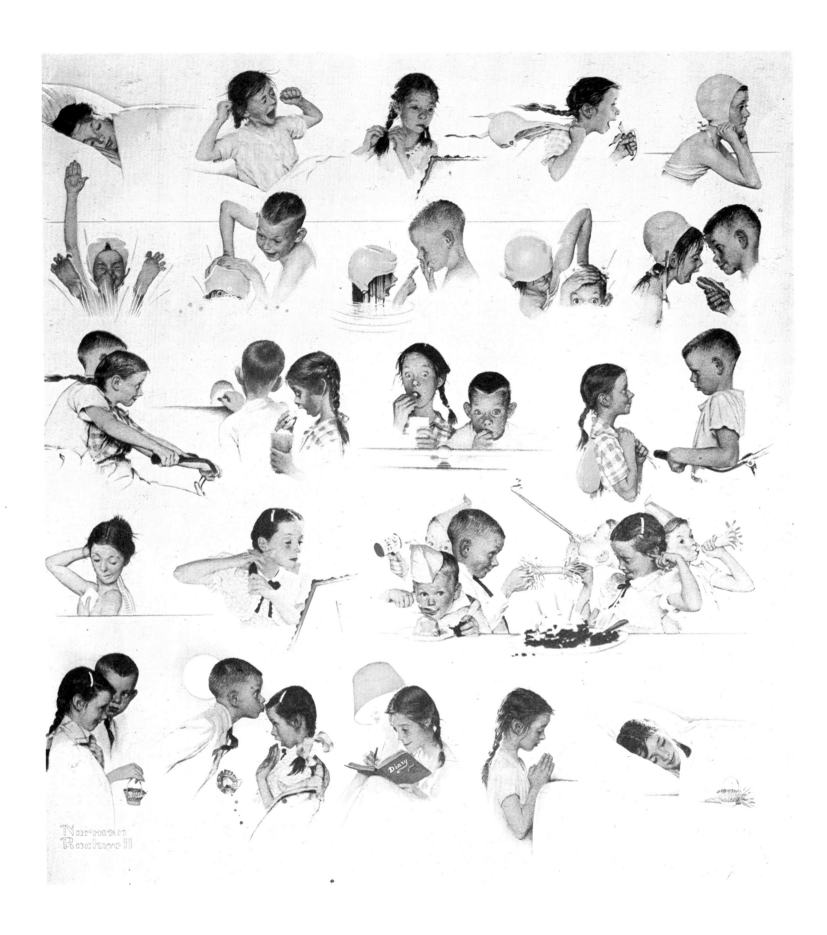

Oats, Peas, Beans, and Barley Grow

3. Waiting for a partner,
   Waiting for a partner,
   Open the ring and take one in
   While we all gaily dance and sing.

She'll Be Comin' Round the Mountain

mountain, She'll be comin' round the mountain when she comes._____
horses, She'll be drivin' six white horses when she comes._____

3. Oh, we'll all go out to meet her when she comes,
   Oh, we'll all go out to meet her when she comes,
   Oh, we'll all go out to meet her,
   Oh, we'll all go out to meet her,
   Oh, we'll all go out to meet her when she comes.

4. Oh, we'll all have sugar and dumplings when she comes,
   Oh, we'll all have sugar and dumplings when she comes,
   Oh, we'll all have sugar and dumplings,
   Oh, we'll all have sugar and dumplings,
   Oh, we'll all have sugar and dumplings when she comes.

5. We'll be singin' hallelujah when she comes,
   We'll be singin' hallelujah when she comes,
   We'll be singin' hallelujah,
   We'll be singin' hallelujah,
   We'll be singin' hallelujah when she comes.

Skip to My Lou

Lou, Lou, skip to my Lou. Skip to my Lou, my dar - ling.

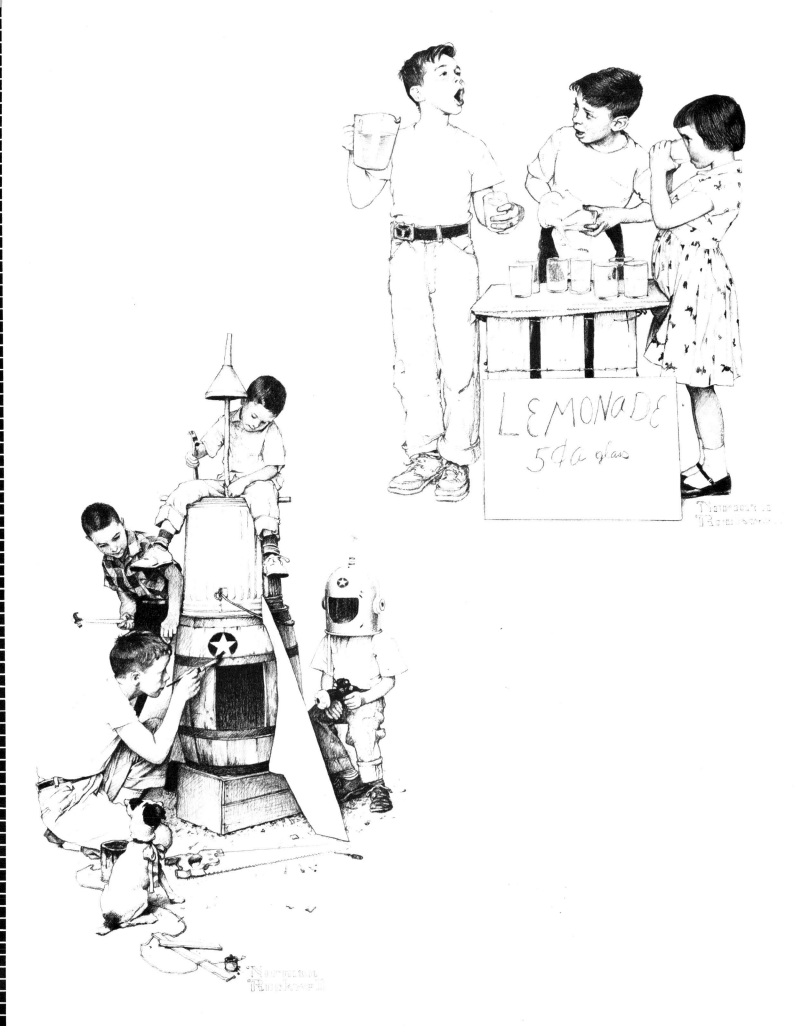

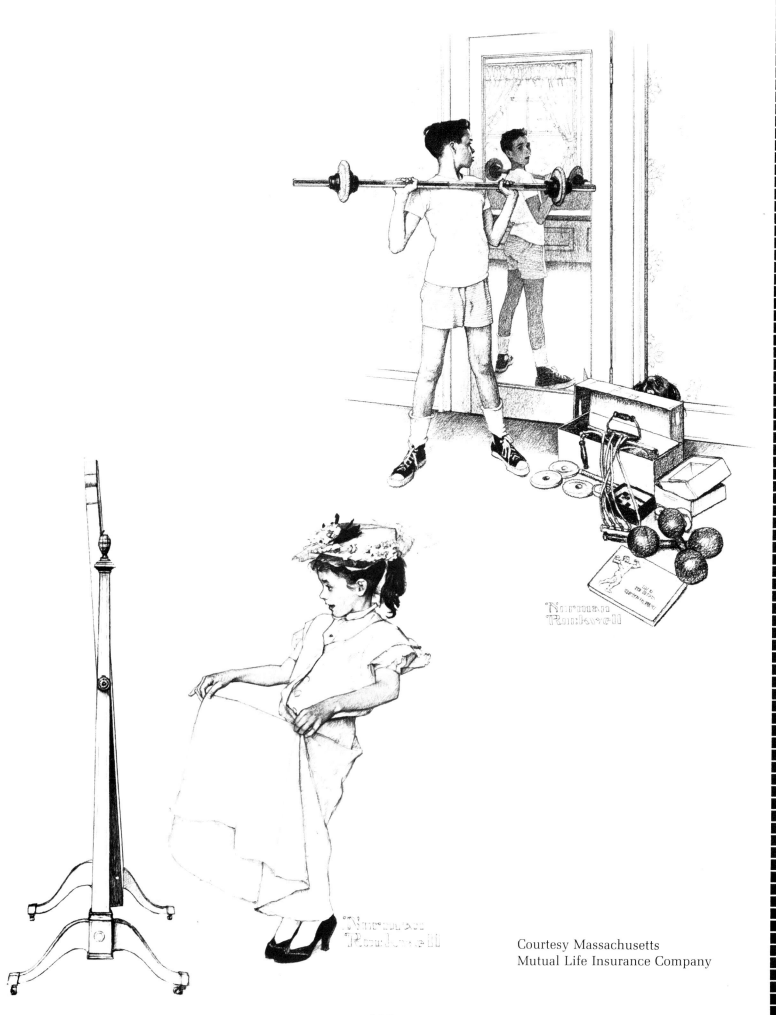

Courtesy Massachusetts
Mutual Life Insurance Company

This Old Man

3. "three," "knee"
4. "four," "door"
5. "five," "hive"
6. "six," "sticks"
7. "seven," "till elev'n"
8. "eight," "gate"
9. "nine," "spine"
10. "ten," "over again"

Old MacDonald Had a Farm

Here a chick, there a chick, eve - ry - where a chick, chick,
Here a quack, there a quack, eve - ry - where a quack, quack,

Alouette

Je te plumerai: (I will pluck your:)
1. La tête (head)
2. Le bec (beak)
3. Le nez (nose)
4. Le dos (back)
5. Les pattes (feet)
6. Le cou (neck)

The Green Grass Grew All Around

and the green grass grew all a - round. Oh, the green grass grew all a -

round, all a - round, and the green grass grew all a - round.   round.

The Bear Went over the Mountain

Guitar Chord Diagrams

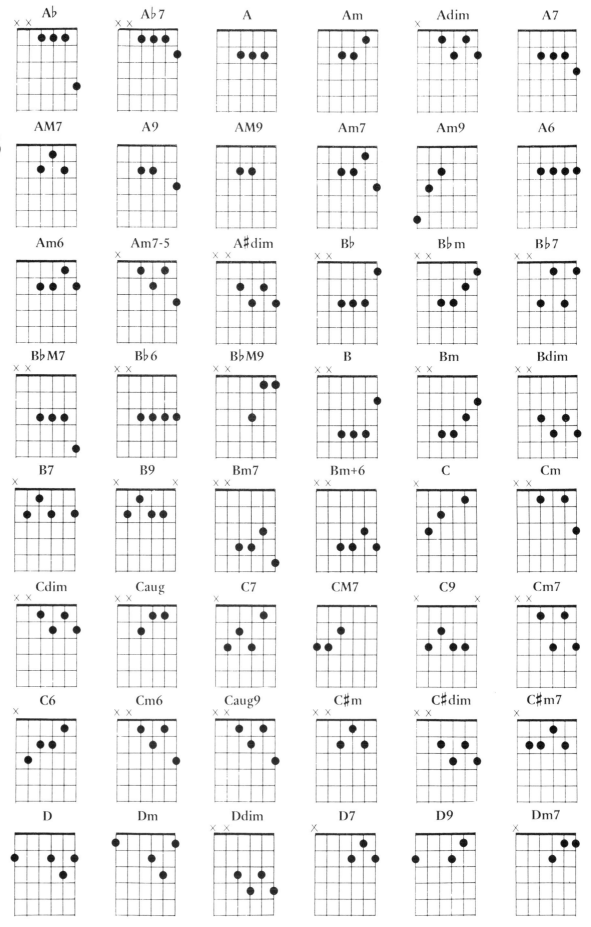

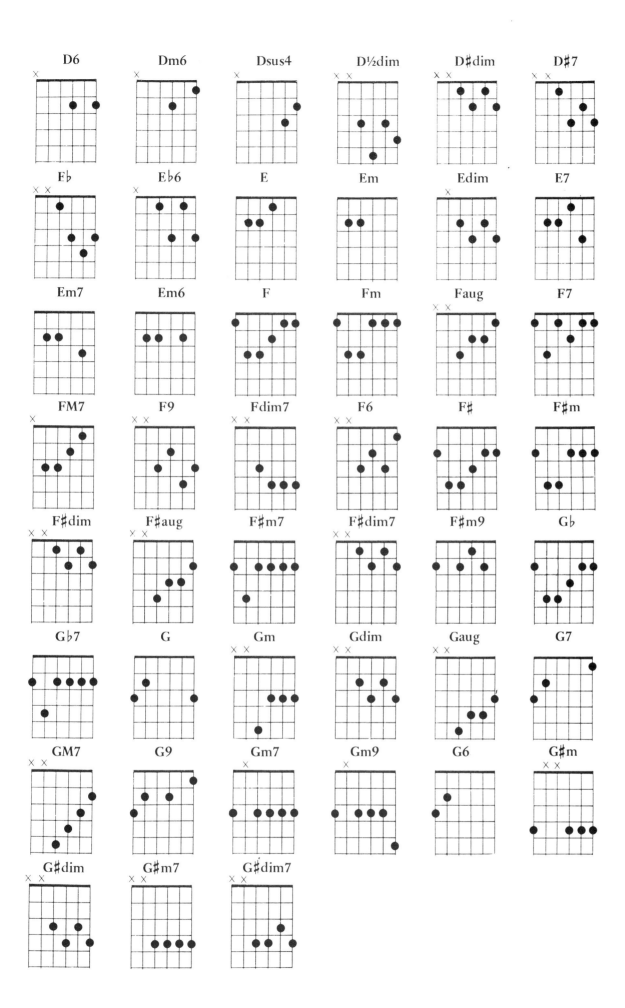

Title Index